If you have ever been busy,
and then stopped to do something
more important,
then you will understand what
happens when...

Text by Lois Rock
Copyright © 1996 Lion Publishing
Illustrations copyright © 1996 Roger Langton

The author asserts the moral right
to be identified as the author of this work

Published by
Lion Publishing plc
Sandy Lane West, Oxford, England
ISBN 0 7459 3102 2
Albatross Books Pty Ltd
PO Box 320, Sutherland, NSW 2232, Australia
ISBN 0 7324 0962 4

First edition 1996
10 9 8 7 6 5 4 3 2 1 0

A catalogue record for this book
is available from the British Library

Printed and bound in Singapore

**This retelling is based on the stories
of Jesus' life in the Bible.**

Jesus Grows Up

Retold by Lois Rock
Illustrations by Roger Langton

A LION BOOK

Mary was Jesus' mother. An angel had said that her son was God's special king. Mary took good care of Jesus.

Her husband, Joseph, made a home for them in Nazareth.

Joseph was a builder and carpenter.
As Jesus grew up, Joseph showed him
how to work with wood and stone.

As he grew up, everybody in the town knew Jesus as the local builder and carpenter.

Jesus' cousin John did something far more exciting. He lived in the desert, but crowds came to hear what he had to say about God.

"Give up your bad ways and live as God wants," John said to them.

If anyone wanted to make a new start,
John baptized them.

He dipped them in the River Jordan as they said goodbye to their old ways...

And lifted them up to show they were
making a new start.

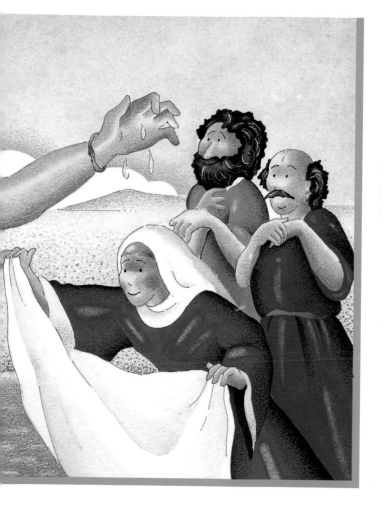

One day, Jesus came and asked to be baptized.

"But you don't need it," said John. "Compared to you, it's me who needs to make a new start for God."

Jesus said he must. And as Jesus came up out of the water, God's voice said, "You are my son. I am pleased with you."

Jesus knew it was time for a change. He had other work to do now. But he spent days thinking about it, wondering if had made the right choice. In some ways, he'd rather be rich, or famous, or important...

But no: he must do as his father God wanted. He must go and tell people about God, and about how to be God's friends.

Down by the lake called Galilee, he saw some fishermen mending their nets.

"Come and help me," he said. "You know what it's like to catch a net full of fish. I need you to help me gather up crowds and crowds of people.

"Because God wants sick people to be made well. God wants sad people to be happy. God wants to welcome people as friends. I'll show you how . . .

And the fishermen left their nets, and went with Jesus.

A Christian prayer

Dear God,
It's easy to be busy
and hardly think of you.
But you call us
to be your friends,
to do the things you want done.
And that is the most important
thing of all.
Amen.